CHALLENGING
Optical Picture
Puzzles

Irit Adler & Shem Levy

Sterling Publishing Co., Inc. New York

Library of Congress Cataloging-in-Publication Data

Adler, Irit.
   Challenging optical picture puzzles / by Irit Adler & Shem Levy.
      p.   cm.
   Condensed version of: Picture puzzles for the super smart / Studio
D. c1985.
   ISBN 0-8069-9440-1
   1. Picture puzzles.   2. Optical illusions.   I. Levy, Shem.   II. Picture
puzzles for the super smart.   III. Title.
GV1507.P47A35   1996
793.73—dc20
                                                          96-30407
                                                            CIP

10   9   8   7   6   5   4   3   2   1.

Published by Sterling Publishing Company, Inc.
387 Park Avenue South, New York, N.Y. 10016
The puzzles in this book have been excerpted from *Picture Puzzles
for the Super Smart* © 1985 by Irit Adler & Shem Levy,
published by Sterling Publishing Co., Inc.
© 1996 by Irit Adler & Shem Levy
Distributed in Canada by Sterling Publishing
% Canadian Manda Group, One Atlantic Avenue, Suite 105
Toronto, Ontario, Canada M6K 3E7
Distributed in Great Britain and Europe by Cassell PLC
Wellington House, 125 Strand, London WC2R 0BB, England
Distributed by Capricorn Link (Australia) Pty Ltd.
P.O. Box 6651, Baulkham Hills, Business Centre, NSW 2153, Australia
Manufactured in the United States of America

Sterling ISBN 0-8069-9440-1

Contents

Before You Begin

First and foremost, this book is meant to be fun. It is intended for game lovers—those who enjoy brainteasers and logic puzzles. Hopefully, it will take you on to new excitements, because you'll need to use a different mode of thinking to solve its problems.

This book doesn't call upon linguistic or verbal skills or your skill with numbers. It touches an entirely different aspect of our minds—our ability to perceive forms and shapes and manipulate them. The puzzles here will also involve you in the process of logical thinking. Solving them will naturally help develop your powers of deduction and lateral thinking as well as spatial perception.

Each chapter of the book will give you a taste of a different type of mind-boggling visual conundrum. The puzzles in each section range from easy to difficult. It is important to start at the beginning and follow them through. As you solve the easier puzzles, you'll come up with the principles and tricks you'll need to tackle the more complex ones!

Good luck!

Crazy Clocks

You're probably used to seeing number progressions such as these:

2–4–6–8—which are 2 apart, or
6–18–54–162—which are each multiplied by 3.

In this chapter, though, you'll find a set of *graphic* progressions. For example, take a look at the puzzle below:

The hand of the clock moves 45° clockwise (a quarter of an hour) in each one of the pictures. In the picture that would naturally follow in sequence, the hand of the clock would point towards 9:00, so you would, of course, select #3 in the multiple choice answers below:

Which one of the five numbered figures should be *the next one* in each of the progressions on the following pages?

1. SWISS CLOCK

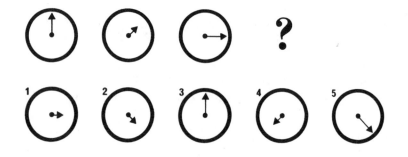

Solution 101

2. ITALIAN CLOCK

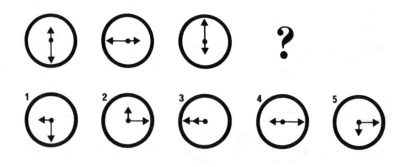

Solution 2

6

3. CLOCKWORK ORANGE

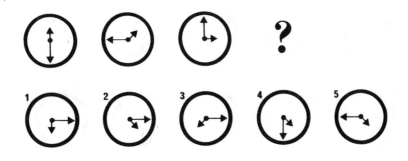

Solution 109

4. TIME BOMB

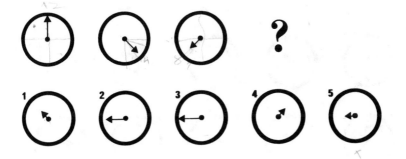

Hint: Notice the length of the hand.

Solution 18

5. GREENWICH TIME

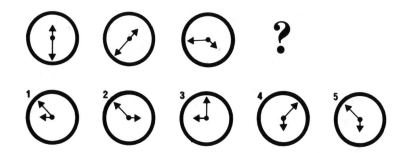

Solution 123

6. BIG BEN

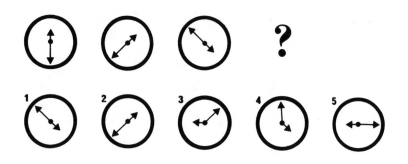

Hint: Both hands advance in the same manner.

Solution 44

7. FOURTH DIMENSION

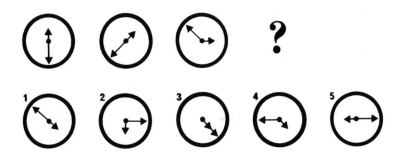

Solution 116

8. QUICK AS A BUNNY

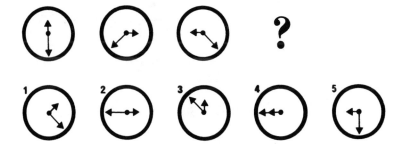

Hint: The long hand goes back and forth.

Solution 9

9. THE CRAZIEST CLOCK

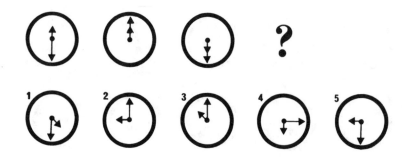

Hint: The short hand starts with 360° degrees.

Solution 88

Peculiar People

You're dealing with graphic progressions here, just as in "Crazy Clocks," the preceding chapter.

Which one of the five numbered figures should be *the next one* in each one of the progressions on the following pages?

10. GROUP DYNAMICS

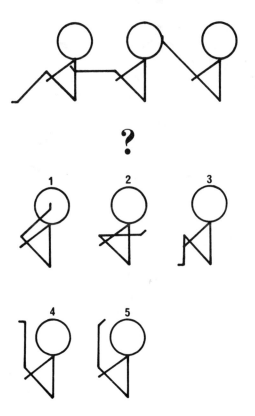

Solution 1

11. HEALTH-OHOLIC

Solution 11

12. UPS AND DOWNS

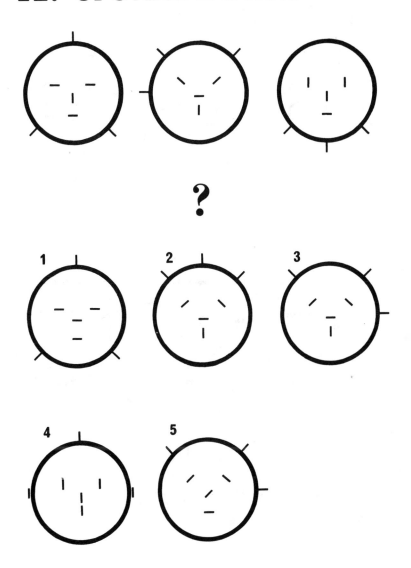

Solution 21

13. THEORY OF EVOLUTION

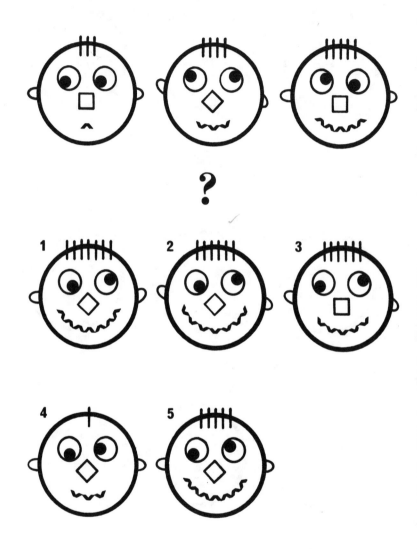

Solution 13

14. THE MAD HATTER

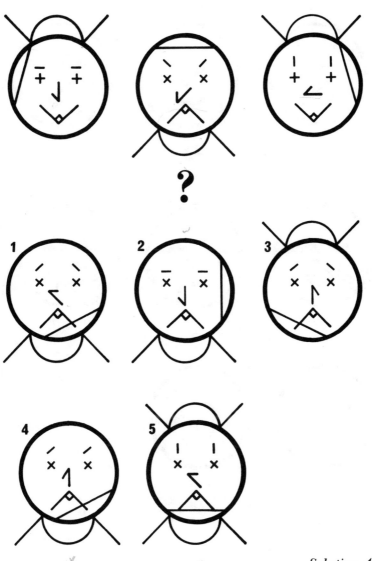

Solution 41

15. POKER FACE

Hint: The eyes have it.

Solution 51

16

Sneaky Shapes

Here are more graphic progressions.

Which one of the five numbered figures should be next in each one of the progressions that follow?

16. BERMUDA TRIANGLE

Hint: Inside out.

Solution 61

17. ANONYMOUS

Solution 71

18. RECTANGLES

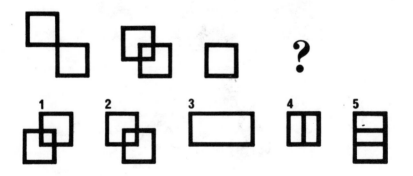

Solution 81

19. CIRCLE IN THE SQUARE

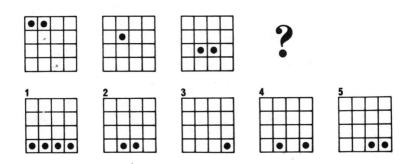

Solution 91

20. SQUARE SHOOTER

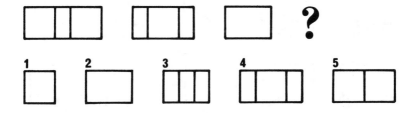

Solution 105

21. CUBBYHOLES

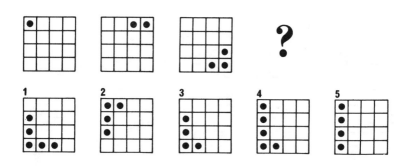

Solution 12

22. ETERNAL TRIANGLES

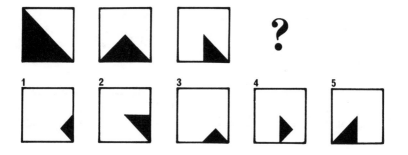

Solution 22

23. THE NUTCRACKER

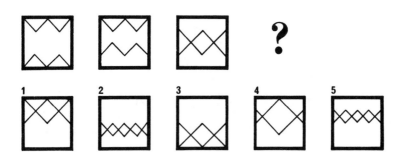

Solution 32

24. ABSTRACTION

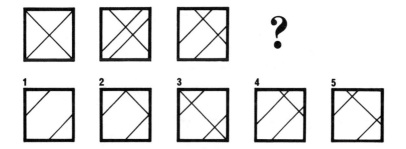

Hint: The lower triangle moves up continuously.

Solution 119

25. TOUGHIE

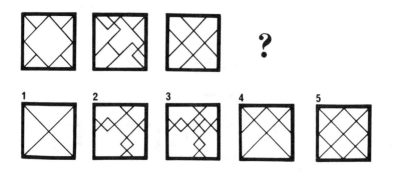

Solution 52

26. SPACE AGE DOMINOES

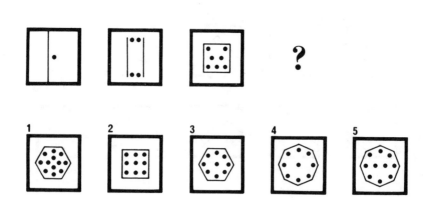

Solution 62

27. ROUNDABOUT

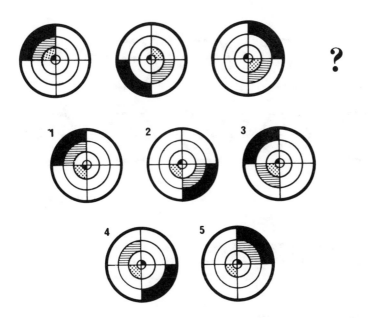

Solution 65

28. TURNING POINT

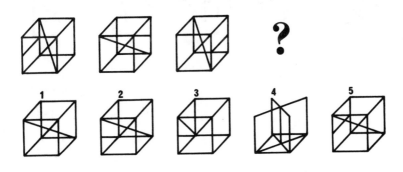

Solution 38

29. FIBUNETZY

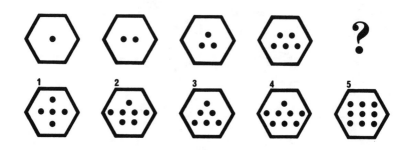

Solution 92

30. CRUSADE

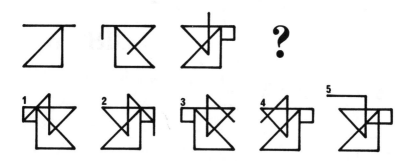

Solution 42

Friendly Relations

Take a look at the diagram to the right. In this set of puzzles, the box marked D is missing.

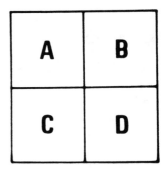

What you have to do is figure out how A and B relate to each other. Then select one of the five answers to make the same relation hold for C and D.

31. "FOURSIES"

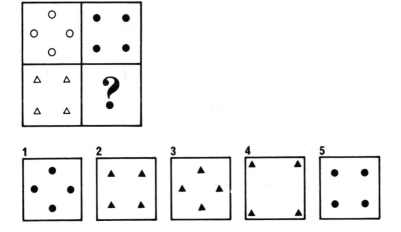

Solution 20

32. NIGHT AND DAY

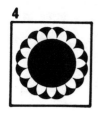 

Solution 72

33. CHORUS LINE

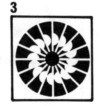

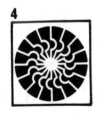

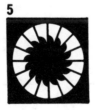

Solution 82

34. ROCK 'N' ROLL

1   2   3   4   5

Solution 92

35. ALICE IN WONDERLAND

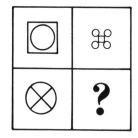

1   2   3   4   5

Solution 3

36. TUMBLEWEED

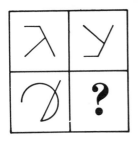

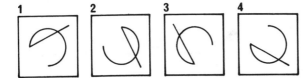

Solution 13

37. FAMILY TIES

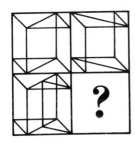

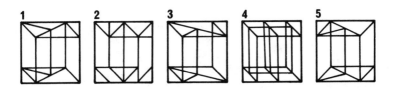

Solution 23

38. BUTCH CASSIDY AND THE SUNDANCE KID

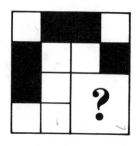

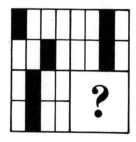

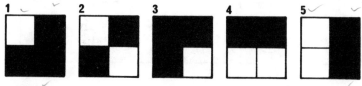

Solution 58

39. HOLMES AND WATSON

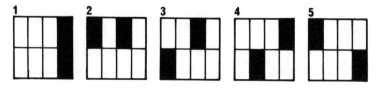

Solution 112

40. BALANCE OF POWER

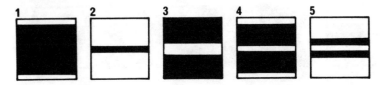

Solution 53

41. RISK

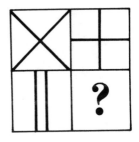

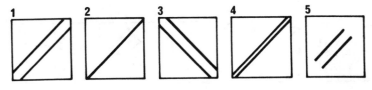

Solution 63

42. MEPHISTOPHELES

Solution 73

43. SPACE SHUTTLE

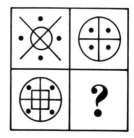

Solution 83

44. THE ULTIMATE TEASER

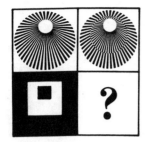

Hint: Try to figure out what portion changes and how.

1   **2**   **3** 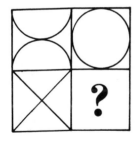 **4**   **5**

Solution 118

45. A DIFFERENT ANGLE

1   **2**   **3**   **4**   **5**

Solution 4

33

Principle

One logical principle relates the three boxes in each horizontal row, when reading from left to right. That same principle applies in all three rows of each puzzle in this chapter. Find it, and you'll be able to select the correct figures for the missing boxes.

46. INGMAR BERGMAN

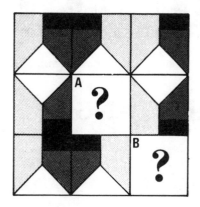

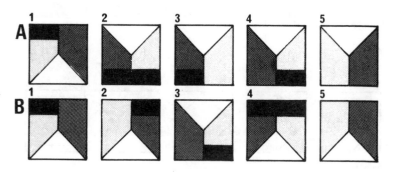

Solution 14

47. DO IT YOURSELF

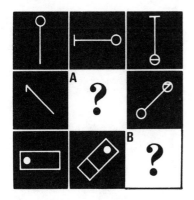

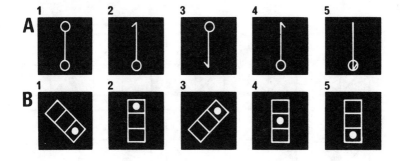

Solution 24

48. BRAIN SQUEEZER

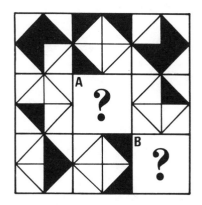

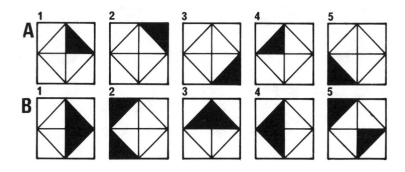

Hint: Folds.

Solution 34

49. I'D RATHER BE SAILING

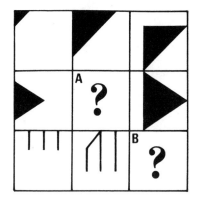

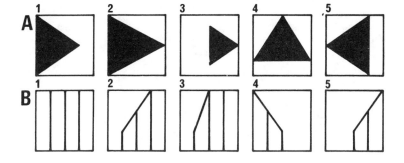

Solution 113

50. CITY LIGHTS

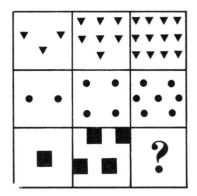

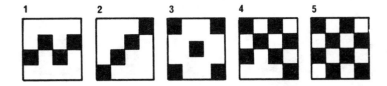

Solution 54

51. ANTENNA

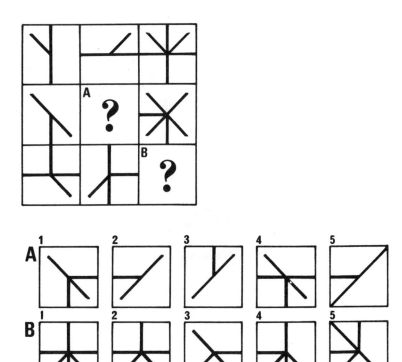

Hint: Additions.

Solution 64

High Principle

These puzzles are similar to the ones in the previous chapter, but here you have four boxes in each row, and four rows of puzzles instead of three. You'll find a missing box in each row, and as usual, five possible answers for each missing box. Which is it?

52. NO SMALL AFFAIR

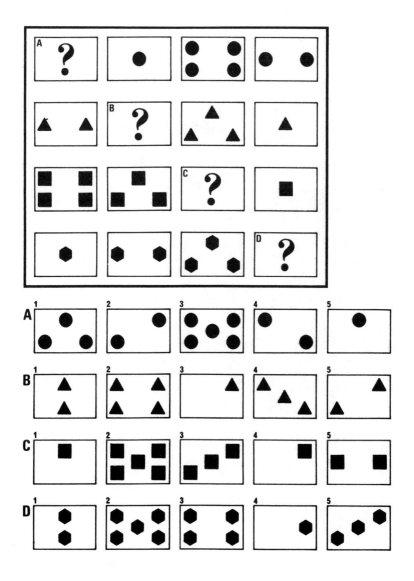

Solution 74

53. WORKING OUT

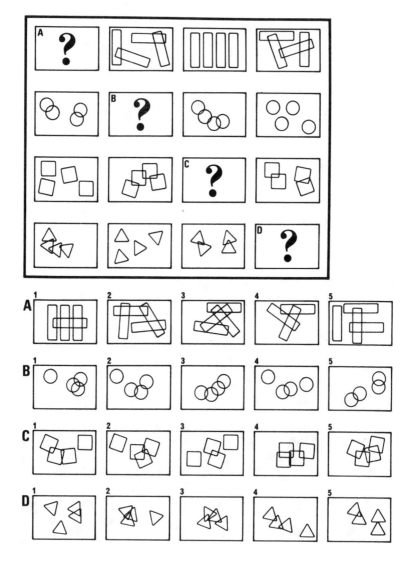

Solution 84

54. A STAR IS BORN

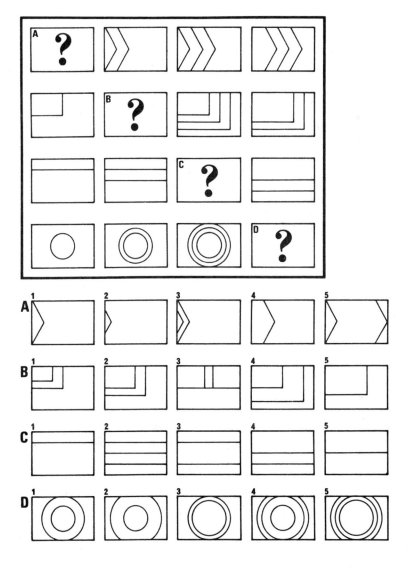

Solution 94

55. PSYCHOMETRICS

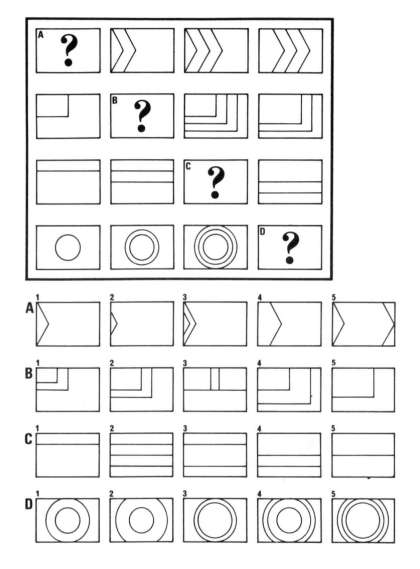

56. CHECKERS

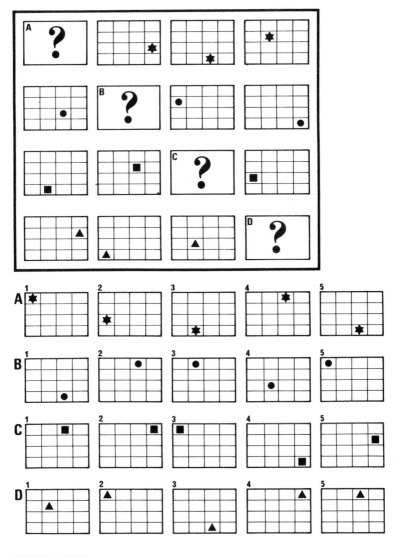

Hint: Positions.

Solution 15

57. KALEIDOSCOPE

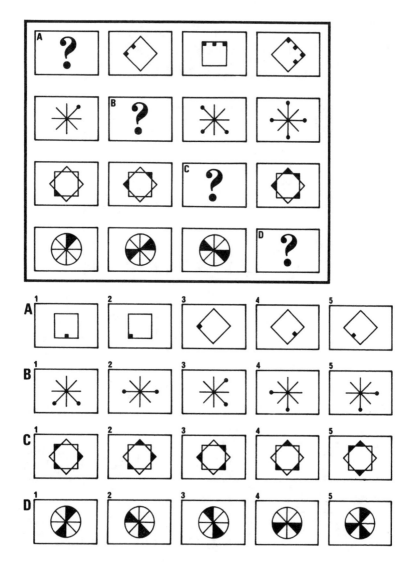

Solution 25

58. GOING TO THE BOLSHOI

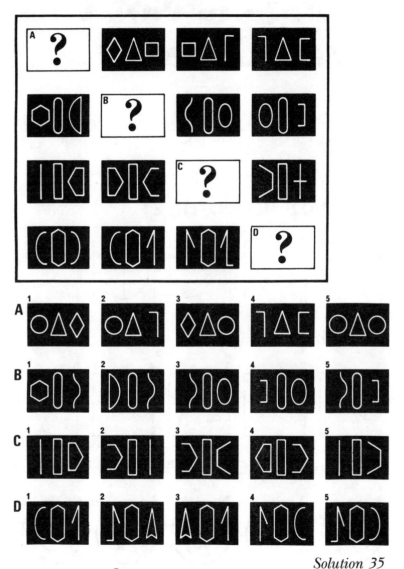

Solution 35

Hint: The middle figures are the easiest.

47

One of These Things Is Not Like the Others . . .

In this chapter, you'll find sets of five figures each. In each set, one figure does not belong. Which one?

59. HALF-MOON STREET
Solution 45

60. PIECE OF CAKE
Solution 55

61. PAWN SHOP
Solution‑114

62. WIRED
Solution 75

63. BREAKING UP
Solution 85

64. FIRST SLICE
Solution 95

65. BEADY EYES
Solution 6

66. CHUNKY
Solution 16

67. SORRY!
Solution 26

68. TINKER TOY
Solution 36

69. TIDDLEDYWINKS
Solution 46

70. TRIPLE A MINUS 2
Solution 56

71. CASTLES IN THE AIR
Solution 115

72. NIGHT AT THE OPERA

Solution 76

1   2   3   4   5

73. "EEEEK!"

Solution 86

1   2   3   4   5

74. DOODLES

Solution 96

1   2   3   4   5

75. DOWSING

Solution 107

1   2   3   4   5

76. ICY

Solution 17

1   2   3   4   5

77. DICE-Y

Solution 27

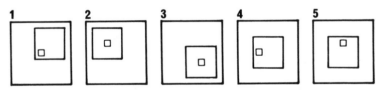

78. JUGGLER

Solution 37

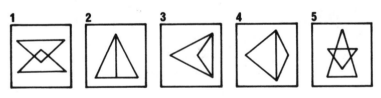

79. THE DEADLY DUO

Solution 47

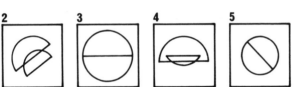

80. "A TISKET A TASKET"

Solution 57

81. PAPER PLANES

Solution 67

82. SOCIAL CLIMBERS

Solution 77

83. ACROBATS

Solution 87

84. TRANSPARENCY

Solution 97

85. DEVIL'S DELIGHT

Solution 8

86. BREAKDANCE

Solution 18

87. TAO

Solution 28

88. CHOPSTICKS

Solution 38

Odd Fellows

As in the previous chapter, one of these things is not like the others. In that chapter you had five separate figures—one of which was different. Here you have one large figure that contains smaller numbered figures within it, and *one* of them is different. Which one?

89. MARY, MARY . . .

Hint: Mind the curves.

Solution 48

90. ATOMIC ACHE

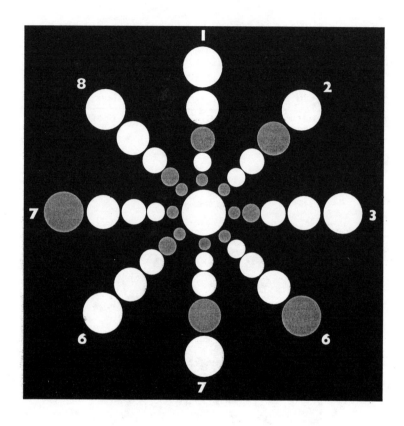

Solution 33

91. CATHERINE WHEEL

Solution 68

92. SNOWFLAKE

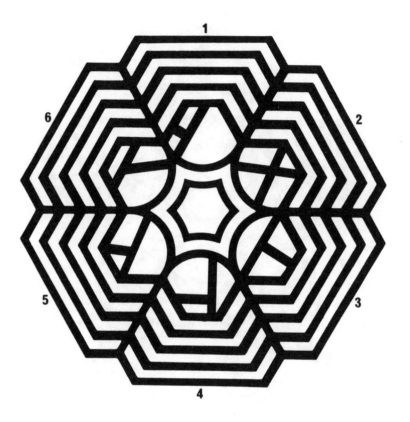

Hint: The short end of the stick.

Solution 78

93. A BRAIN SHORT CIRCUIT

Hint: Look at each branch when it is straight in front of you (turn the puzzle as you look).

Solution 108

Higher Principle

These puzzles are similar to those in "Principle" (page 34), but tougher.

94. BUDAPEST

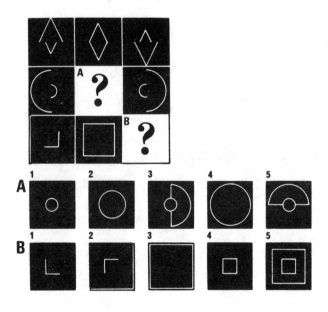

Hint: In and out.

Solution 98

95. WIZARD OF OZ

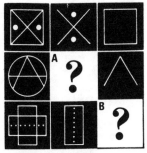

Hint: Add backwards.

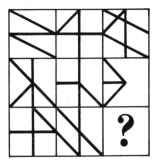

Solution 9

96. SYNAPSE KILLER

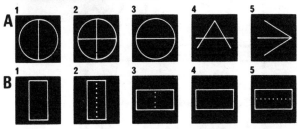

Hint: Eliminate the common qualities.

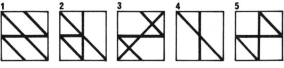

Solution 19

97. BATES MOTEL

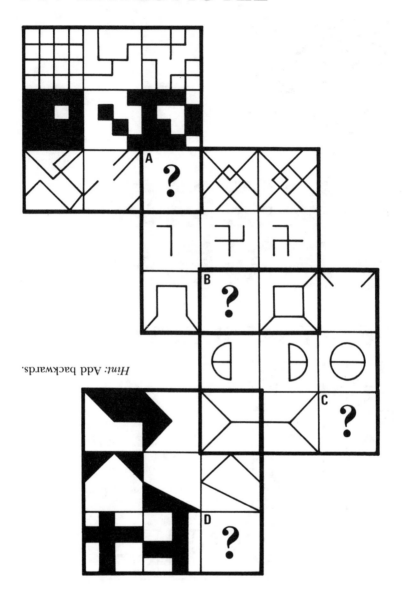

Hint: Add backwards.

62

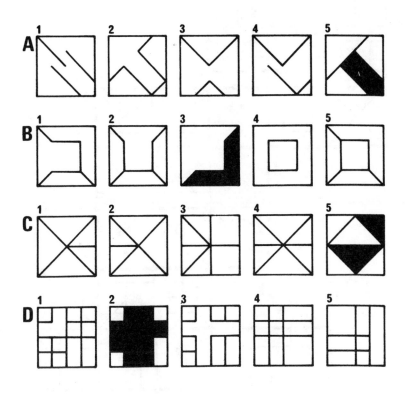

98. THE FRENCH CONNECTION

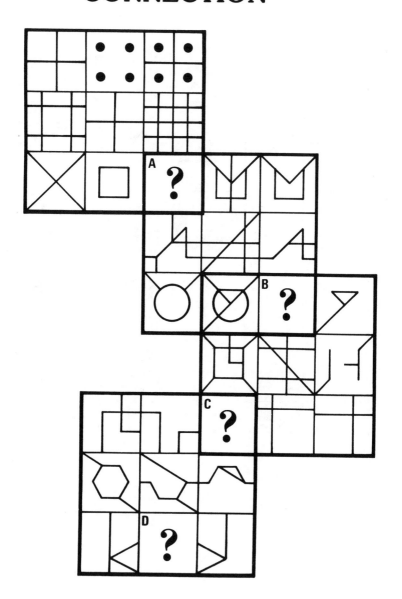

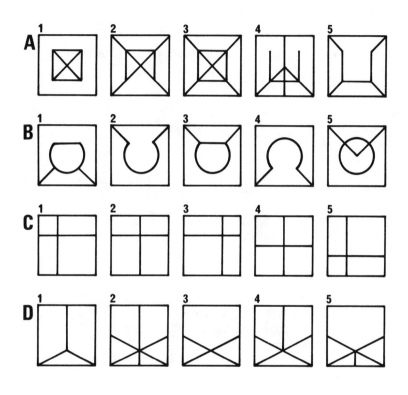

Solution 39

Diabolical Designs

Remember the progressions in "Crazy Clocks," "Peculiar People," and "Sneaky Shapes"? These "Diabolical Designs" are the same sort of puzzles—squared!

99. DUCK SOUP

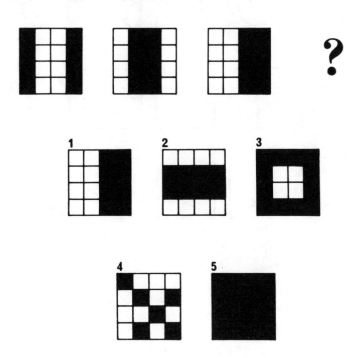

Solution 49

100. HEX

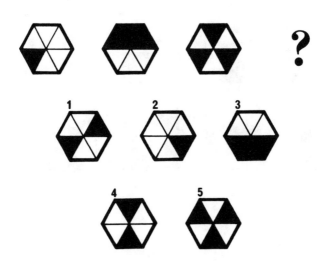

Hint: There is more than one dark triangle in the first position.

Solution 59

101. MOROCCO

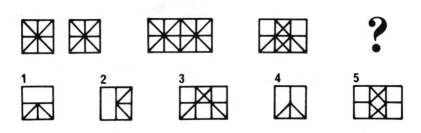

Hint: See "Anonymous" (page 18), but find the added complication!

Solution 69

102. DUNGEONS

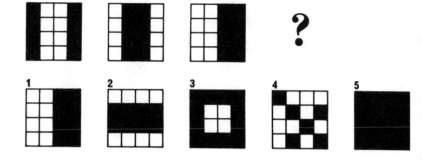

Solution 79

103. PARACHUTE

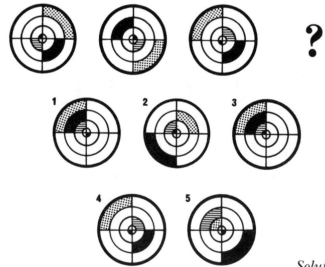

Solution 89

104. DRAGONS

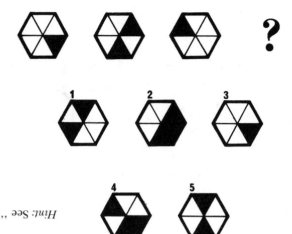

Hint: See "Hex."

Solution 99

105. TOWERS

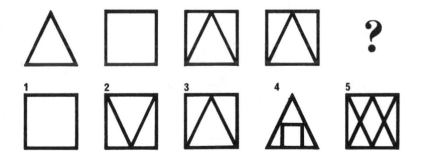

Hint: See "Fibunetzy" on page 24.

Solution 10

106. ROUND DANCE

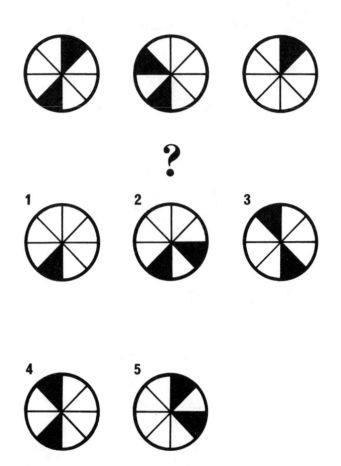

Solution 88

Intimate Relations

As in "Friendly Relations" (page 25), Box D is missing here. Your task is to select it from the five possible answers. But, as you will see, "Intimate Relations" are more complex than friendly ones.

107. BEMUSED WITH BULFINCH

Solution 30

108. SZECHUAN AND HUNAN

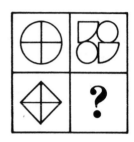

1   2   3   4   5

Solution 40

109. ORIGAMI

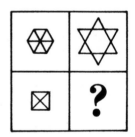

Hint: Unfolding.

1   2   3   4   5

Solution 50

110. PUFF THE MAGIC DRAGON

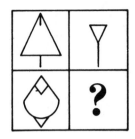

Solution 60

111. KITES

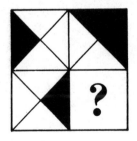

Hint: Intuition doesn't always prove out.

Solution 70

112. MANIPULATION

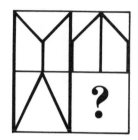

Solution 80

113. CANTERBURY TAIL

Solution 90

114. THE MUMMY'S CURSE

Hint: See "Canterbury Tail" (page 74).

1   2   3   4   5

Solution 100

115. WITCHES

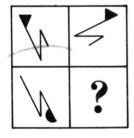

1   2   3   4   5

Solution 93

Highest Principle

This chapter is similar to "Principle" (page 34). The same principle holds true for every line of the puzzle.

116. GONE WITH THE WIND

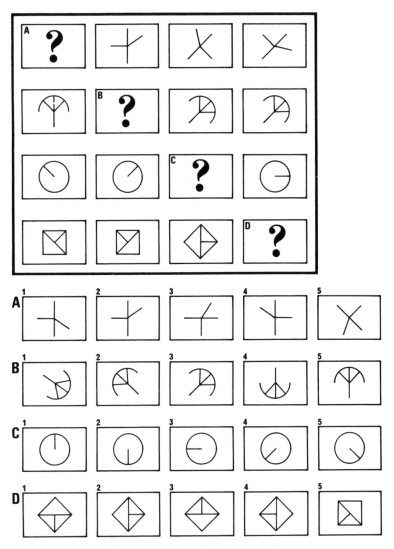

Hint: Flip and turn.

Solution 102

77

117. SINBAD THE SAILOR

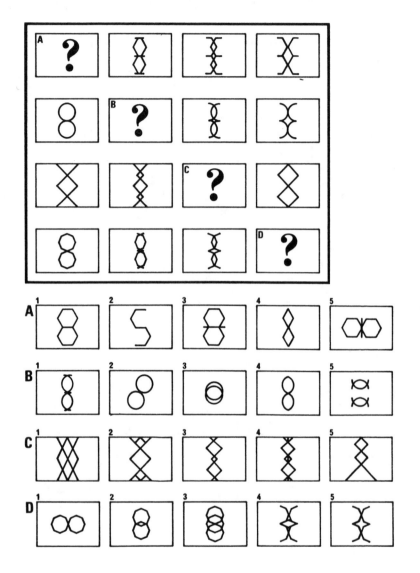

Solution 17

118. LAWRENCE OF ARABIA

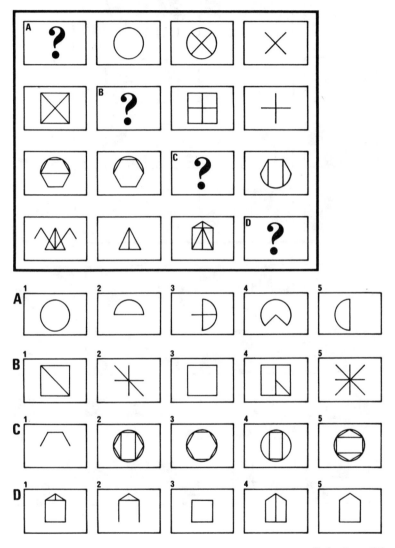

Solution 66

119. MARY POPPINS

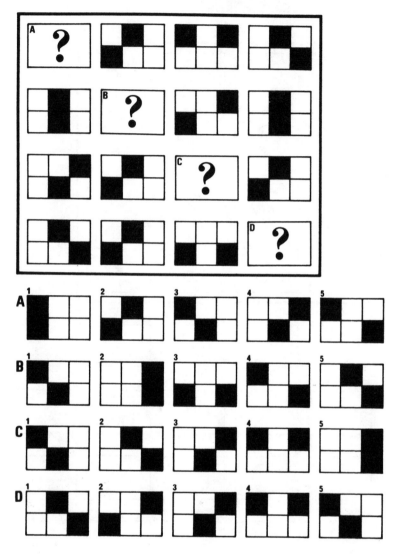

Hint: Constant movement.

Solution 117

120. ABBOTT AND COSTELLO MEET FRANKENSTEIN

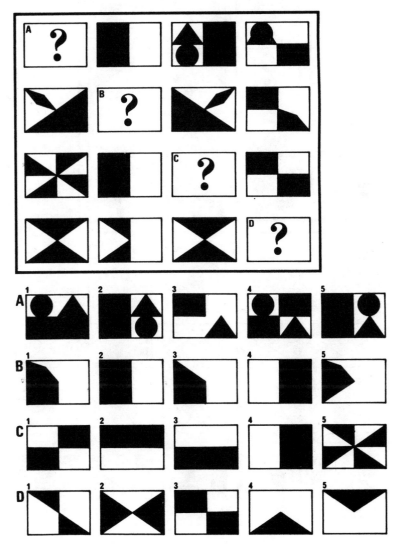

121. PLAY IT AGAIN, SAM

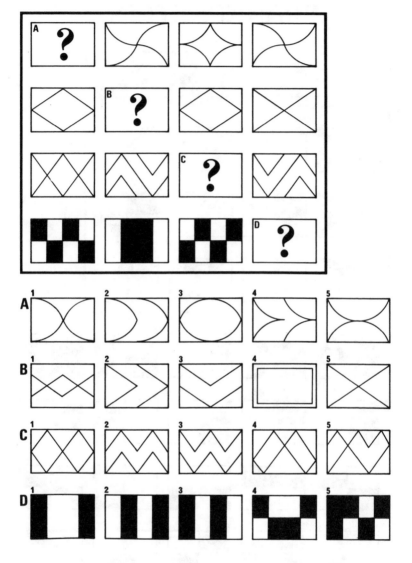

Solution 43

122. TARZAN, KING OF THE JUNGLE

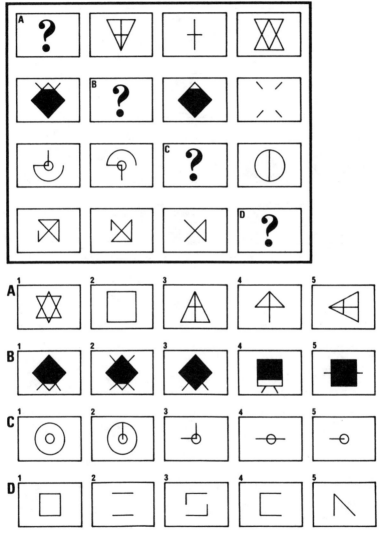

Solution 105

123. THE THREE STOOGES

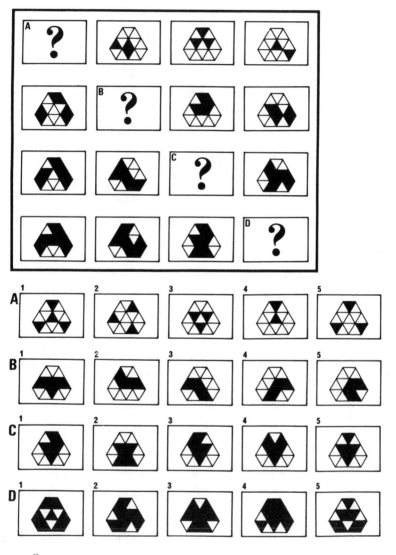

Hint: Think of three hexagons.

Solution 110

84

Answers

1 Group Dynamics
#5. The shin bone moves 45° each time. *Puzzle 10*

2 Italian Clock
#4. *Puzzle 2*

3 Alice in Wonderland
#5. Outer figure shrinks and inner figure surrounds it four times. *Puzzle 35*

4 A Different Angle
#3. *Puzzle 45*

5 Psychometrics
A #2. B #5. C #1. D #2. The black dots advance in constant paces from one position to the next. The angles advance in an arithmetic series where d = 1 (e.g., 1-2-3-4). *Puzzle 55*

6 Beady Eyes
#3. In all but #3, the innermost circle is centered in the outer circle. *Puzzle 65*

7 Abbott and Costello Meet Frankenstein
A #2. B #1. C #5. D #1. From the first position to the second: the right half of the box flips sideways onto the left side. From the second to the third positions: the half that was originally on the left side of the box now flips sideways onto the right side. From the third to fourth positions: the lower half of the left half flips upwards and the upper half of the right half flips downwards. *Puzzle 120*

8 Devil's Delight
#3. The only shape with more than eight intersections is #3. *Puzzle 85*

9 Quick as a Bunny
#4. The short hand moves 90°, 180°, 360°. The long hand moves 45° clockwise, 90° counterclockwise, 135° clockwise. *Puzzle 8*

10 Towers
#3. This is based on the famous Fibunetzy progression of 1, 2, 3, 5, 8 (each item is the sum of the two items preceding it). *Puzzle 105*

11 Health-oholic
#4. The legs move 90° from one position to the next. *Puzzle 11*

12 Cubbyholes
#5. Skip one and add one. *Puzzle 21*

13 Tumbleweed
#2. Figure turns 180° and then turns aside. *Puzzle 36*

14 Ingmar Bergman
A #3. B #2. *Puzzle 46*

15 Checkers
A #1. B #3. C #2. D #5. Each black figure (star, triangle, circle, square) is positioned in a different place both horizontally and vertically. *Puzzle 56*

16 Chunky
#4. Only #4 does not have at least two parallel surfaces.

Puzzle 66

17 Sinbad the Sailor
A #1. B #1. C #3. D #5. Make an imaginary vertical cut in the middle of each figure in the left box. Then move the two cut sections towards each other as the puzzle progresses to the right. *Puzzle 117*

18 Time Bomb
#5. The hand moves 135°, then 90°, then 45°, and as it moves, it shrinks. *Puzzle 4*

19 Synapse Killer
#1. The boxes on the right column are formed by the addition of the two other boxes in the line—*minus* the lines the two boxes have in common.

Puzzle 96

20 "Foursies"
#3. *Puzzle 31*

21 Ups and Downs
#3. *Puzzle 12*

22 Eternal Triangles
#3. *Puzzle 22*

23 Family Ties
#3. *Puzzle 37*

24 Do It Yourself
A #2. B #5. The upper line turns 90° each time; the middle line, 45°; the lower line, 135°. *Puzzle 47*

25 Kaleidoscope
A #2. B #5. C #1. D #3. There is a 45° move from each position to the next. A black figure (a square, dot, triangle, etc.) is added at a constant interval in each row. *Puzzle 57*

26 Sorry!
#5. The figure in #5 is the only one intersected twice.

Puzzle 67

27 Dice-y
#4. Only #4 is not a prime number. *Puzzle 77*

28 Tao
#5. All but #5 are closed loops.

Puzzle 87

29 Bates Motel
A #1. The left box is a simple addition of the middle and right boxes in the same row.

B #5. B, as a middle box, is the sum of the figure in the left column plus the same figure turned 90°.

C #4. The right column is the sum of the middle and left boxes minus their common lines, so C is the simple sum of the other two boxes.

D #1. The right column boxes are the contours of the solid black figures in the left and middle columns.

Puzzle 97

30   Bemused with Bulfinch
#1.   *Puzzle 107*

31   Theory of Evolution
#2.   *Puzzle 13*

32   The Nutcracker
#5. The lower lines move up, then the upper lines move down (the third position). Finally, the lower lines move up again.   *Puzzle 23*

33   Atomic Ache
#1. Only #1 has one white circle between the two gray ones.
Puzzle 90

34   Brain Squeezer
A #5. B #4. Fold out from the first position to the second. Double-fold in from the second to the third.   *Puzzle 48*

35   Going to the Bolshoi
A #1. B #2. C #3. D #2. The figures on the right flip sideways and move to the left side of the preceding position. The next figure on the right is always a new one (that's why D #5 is incorrect).   *Puzzle 58*

36   Tinker Toy
#5. Only #5 is not symmetrical.
Puzzle 68

37   Juggler
#2. Only #2 has three different kinds of figures.   *Puzzle 78*

38   Turning Point
#2.   *Puzzle 28*

39   The French Connection
A #3. Addition. B #2. The right column boxes are the common lines of the left and middle boxes. C #3. The right column boxes are the same as the left ones on the same row—minus their common lines. D #5. The middle boxes are the sum of the right and left boxes minus their common lines.   *Puzzle 98*

40   Szechuan and Hunan
#3.   *Puzzle 108*

41   The Mad Hatter
#1.   *Puzzle 14*

42   Crusade
#3. The figure turns from side to side as lines of equal length are added to each side in constant angles.   *Puzzle 30*

43   Play It Again, Sam
A #3. B #5. C #1. D #1. Make imaginary vertical and horizontal cuts through the middle of the boxes on the left. Each box is now divided into four quarters. The four quarters move clockwise one step

at a time from one position to the next. *Puzzle 121*

44 Big Ben
#5. Both hands advance at the rate of 45°, 90°, 135°.
Puzzle 6

45 Half-Moon Street
#5. *Puzzle 59*

46 Tiddledywinks
#5. All but #5 have either one black or one white figure.
Puzzle 69

47 The Deadly Duo
#4. All except #4 contain two halves of circles *Puzzle 79*

48 Mary, Mary . . .
#1. Only #1 has two curved lines. The others have one curved and one straight line.
Puzzle 89

49 Duck Soup
#1. The first black squares on the left advance to the right. The ones on the right move back and forth—one position to the left, then one to the right, etc. *Puzzle 99*

50 Origami
#1. *Puzzle 109*

51 Poker Face
#2. *Puzzle 15*

52 Toughie
#3. From first to second position, the lower lines move up and the left lines move right. From second to third position, the upper lines move down and the left lines move right. From third to fourth position (answer #3), the lower lines move down and the left lines move right again. *Puzzle 25*

53 Balance of Power
#2. Negative. *Puzzle 40*

54 City Lights
#5. Upper row: $3 + 4 = 7$; $7 + 5 = 12$. Middle row: $2 + 2 = 4$; $4 + 3 = 7$. The second number you add is always one more than the number in the first box. Therefore, $1 + 3 = 4$; $4 + 4 = 8$. *Puzzle 50*

55 Piece of Cake
#1. Only #1 has a 90° (right) angle. The others all are equilateral triangles. *Puzzle 60*

56 Triple A Minus 2
#3. All but #3 show the same figure in different positions. Although #3 is the same figure, it is flipped to its mirror image. *Puzzle 70*

57 "A Tisket a Tasket"
#1. All except #1 have either the smallest square in the middle of the medium one or the medium square in the middle of the largest (outside) one.
Puzzle 80

58 Butch Cassidy and the Sundance Kid
#1. Negative. *Puzzle 38*

59 Hex
#1. There are actually three dark triangles in the first position. One advances clockwise one step at a time. The second advances two steps at a time, and the third advances three steps at a time. *Puzzle 100*

60 Puff the Magic Dragon
#5. The large shape flips over and diminishes. The two lines (or, in the second case, angles) appear immediately below it. *Puzzle 110*

61 Bermuda Triangle
#4. *Puzzle 16*

62 Space Age Dominoes
#5. The lines multiply each time. The dots add three. *Puzzle 26*

63 Risk
#5. The figure moves 45° and shrinks. *Puzzle 41*

64 Antenna
A #2. B #1. The figure at the right is the sum of the left and middle figures in the same row. *Puzzle 51*

65 Roundabout
#2. The black outer circle moves clockwise 3-2-1. The striped circle moves 2-4-8. The dotted circle moves one each time. The black inner circle remains in the same position. *Puzzle 27*

66 Lawrence of Arabia
A #1. B #3. C #2. D #1. The figures in the boxes second from the left are the common lines of those on their left and right sides. The figures in the boxes second from the right are the addition of those from the right and left sides of them. *Puzzle 118*

67 Paper Planes
#2. All but #2 have two isosceles triangles. *Puzzle 81*

68 Catherine Wheel
#4. Only #4 contains an even number of dots. (It's also the only one with an equal number of dots on each side of the leaf). *Puzzle 91*

69 Morocco
#1. *Puzzle 101*

70 Kites
#2. *Puzzle 111*

71 Anonymous
#1. The two As move toward each other at a steady pace until they merge. *Puzzle 17*

72 Night and Day
#3. Negative. *Puzzle 32*

73 Mephistopheles
#4. Turn 180°. Since the lower figure is symmetrical, it remains the same. *Puzzle 42*

74 No Small Affair
A #1. B #2. C #5. D #3.
Puzzle 52

75 Wired
#4. Only #4 is a different figure from the rest. *Puzzle 62*

76 Night at the Opera
#3. Only in #3 the lines don't extend from adjacent angles.
Puzzle 72

77 Rock 'n' Roll
#5. *Puzzle 34*

78 Snowflake
#2. All but #2 have one longer and one shorter line.
Puzzle 92

79 Dungeons
#5. The three black squares on the left have one additional square added to them in every position, moving upwards and right. The one black square on the right moves left, with one square added in each position.
Puzzle 102

80 Manipulation
#3. Move the left part of the shape to the right and the right part to the left.
Puzzle 112

81 Rectangles
#2. The upper square moves toward the smaller one. In the third position they merge, and then the squares keep moving down. *Puzzle 18*

82 Chorus Line
#2. Negative. *Puzzle 33*

83 Space Shuttle
#4. *Puzzle 43*

84 Working Out
A #5. B #2. C #1. D #4. The only combination that appears in every answer and is missing in every row: a picture in which three figures are linked and a fourth is detached.
Puzzle 53

85 Tarzan, King of the Jungle
A #3. B #1. C #5. D #4. From the first position to the second, there's a 180° turn and a flip sideways. The third box is the second minus the common lines of the second, and the fourth turned 180° (this turn is evident only in the second row). *Puzzle 122*

86 "Eeeek!"
#2. All but #2 show the same figure in different positions. Although #2 is the same figure, it is flipped to its mirror image. *Puzzle 73*

87 Acrobatics
#5. All but #5 are made up of two identical figures. *Puzzle 83*

88   The Craziest Clock
#2. The short hand moves 360°, 180°, 90°. The long hand moves 180° each time.

Puzzle 9

89   Parachute
#4. The inner striped circle advances counterclockwise: 45°, 90°, 180°. The middle black circle advances clockwise: 180°, 90°, 45°. The outer dotted circle advances clockwise 45° each time.   *Puzzle 103*

90   Canterbury Tail
#4. Negative image with a clockwise 90° turn leaves the shape unchanged.   *Puzzle 113*

91   Circle in the Square
#4. The left dot moves down diagonally, while the right one moves straight down. In the second position, they happen to merge.   *Puzzle 19*

92   Fibunetzy
#4. This is the famous Fibunetzy progression, in which each item is the sum of the two previous ones.   *Puzzle 29*

93   Witches
#4. The line shape turns clockwise 90°. The black shape flips over to the other side.

Puzzle 115

94   A Star Is Born
A #1. B #2. C #2. D #5. In the third position, the figure is complete. In the fourth position, it simply advances. In the upper row it advances to the right. In the second row it advances diagonally. In the third row it moves downward and in the fourth row it advances outward.   *Puzzle 54*

95   First Slice
#2. Only in #2 does the line move downwards.   *Puzzle 64*

96   Doodles
#3. Only #3 does not include an acute angle.   *Puzzle 74*

97   Transparency
#3. Only in #3 the two equal shapes are not parallel to each other.   *Puzzle 84*

98   Budapest
A #2. B #2. One figure constantly gets smaller while the other grows.   *Puzzle 94*

99   Dragons
#3. There are, in fact, two black triangles in the first position. One advances clockwise and the other counterclockwise: one, two, three positions each time.   *Puzzle 104*

100   The Mummy's Curse
#5.   *Puzzle 114*

101   Swiss Clock
#2.   *Puzzle 1*

102 Gone with the Wind

A #4. B #5. C #1. D #3. From first position to the second, the figure flips sideways into its own mirror image. From second to third, it flips sideways again and turns 45° clockwise. From third to fourth positions, the figure flips upside down and then turns counterclockwise 90°.

Puzzle 116

103 Breakdance

#2. All but #2 are drawn in one continuous line. *Puzzle 86*

104 Icy

#4. Only #4 lacks a diamond shape in the middle.

Puzzle 76

105 Square Shooter

#4. See "Rectangles" and "Anonymous." *Puzzle 20*

106 Round Dance

#2. One black triangle advances four steps each time, and the other advances two steps each time. *Puzzle 106*

107 Dowsing

#4. Only in #4 are the three dots arranged in a straight line. *Puzzle 75*

108 A Brain Short Circuit

#2. The black parts of each branch—when you put them together—form a perfect black circle. But in #2 one seg-

ment of the circle would be left over; it has been blackened twice. *Puzzle 93*

109 Clockwork Orange

#2. *Puzzle 3*

110 The Three Stooges

A #5. B #3. C #1. D #2. The structure that appears in each box is actually made up of three hexagons that partially overlap: one at the lower left, one at the lower right, and one at the top. The black triangles in each one of the hexagons move differently, but they all move clockwise: one step at a time in the lower left one; two steps in the lower right one; and three steps at a time in the top hexagon. *Puzzle 123*

111 Wizard of Oz

A #1. B #1. Each box in the left column is the sum of the box in the right column and the one in the middle column turned 90°. *Puzzle 95*

112 Holmes and Watson

#4. The upper black rectangle moves two positions to the right. The lower one stays in its original position. *Puzzle 39*

113 I'd Rather Be Sailing

A #1. B #2. The constant moves continuously—in the upper line diagonally; in the middle line, to the right; in the lower line, down.   *Puzzle 49*

middle part changes to its negative image.   *Puzzle 44*

114   Pawn Shop
#5. Only #5 has three circles that intersect.   *Puzzle 61*

115   Castles in the Air
#2. Only #2 is not a hexagon.
    Puzzle 71

116   Fourth Dimension
#3. The short hand moves 45° at a time. The long hand moves 45°, 90°, 180°.
    Puzzle 7

117   Mary Poppins
A #3. B #4. C #3. D #1. In the top row, the black boxes advance clockwise one square from one position to the next. In the second row, two squares at a time; three at a time in the third row; and four squares at a time in the fourth row.
    Puzzle 119

118   The Ultimate Teaser
#3. The inner and outer part remain the same. Only the

119   Abstraction
#2. Lower triangle constantly moves up. Left triangle constantly moves to the right. Upper triangle constantly moves up and finally disappears, as does the right triangle.
    Puzzle 24

120   Chopsticks
#2. All but #2 have two equal lines.   *Puzzle 88*

121   Breaking Up
#1. Only #1 is missing a triangle.   *Puzzle 63*

122   Social Climbers
#1. Only #1 has no black dot in the small triangle.
    Puzzle 82

123   Greenwich Time
#1. The short hand moves 45°, 90°, 135°. The long hand moves 45° in each picture.
    Puzzle 5

ABOUT THE AUTHORS

Early in her career, graphic artist Irit Adler taught courses in graphic arts in her native Tel Aviv. She later became chief art director for one of Israel's largest advertising agencies. Irit designs graphic games and tests.

Also a native of Tel Aviv, Shem Levy studied political science and psychology, and later did graduate work at the University of Chicago in the U.S. During that period and since, he has been researching psychometric (intelligence) tests, which he feels are culture-biased and should not be used (as they are in many countries, including Israel) to determine who gets accepted to educational programs at any level. He founded "High Q," one of the leading companies in Israel. A school in which people are prepared to take university entrance exams and also such standardized tests as the GMAT, TOEFL, GRE and SAT, High Q now has 20 branches in Israel, and teaches in several high schools and colleges. It also has a branch in Sweden. High Q has also developed a number of books, seven of which are sold in bookstores.

High Q has developed a "daughter" company called TISOM (Tel Aviv International School of Management), which offers an MBA program. Irit and Shem are the first educators to get permission to establish a private university in Israel. The faculty is made up of leading professors from all over the world. All the teaching is done in English.

Irit and Shem are married and have two children, a boy and a girl.

Index